**This book is dedicated
to the Flying Santas and their faithful helpers,
past, present, and future.**

With very special thanks to Joanna Robinson,
George Morgan, Brian Tague, and William Wincapaw III

Published by

Calling Crane Books
P.O. Box 642
Nevada City, California 95959

Illustrations were painted with acrylic watercolor

Library of Congress Cataloging in Publication Data
Library of Congess Control Number - 2002091657
McHugh, Joe / The Flying Santa /
Summary / A true story from Maine of a 1929 pilot who was saved in a storm by seeing the light from a lighthouse and decided to reward the familes of the lighthouses with Christmas gifts dropped from his plane, a tradition that continues on to this day.

ISBN 0-9619943-3-9 (lib.bid.)

The Flying Santa

A TRUE STORY

by Joe McHugh

Illustrated by Paula Blasius McHugh

Calling
Crane

P.O. Box 642
Nevada City, CA 95959

www. callingcrane.com

The frenzied, wind-driven snow of a winter storm battered Bill Wincapaw's small airplane. Everything around him was white, and he couldn't tell where he was going. Desperately he struck the glass face of his compass, but the frozen needle refused to move. Was he flying over land or heading farther and farther out to sea? Unlike the compass, the needle on the fuel gauge worked only too well, and it showed him he was running dangerously low on gasoline — an hour, maybe less, and the engine would sputter and die. Bill was a courageous man, but as he thought of his wife and ten-year-old son, his heart almost gave way to despair.

"Is this how it's all going to end?" Bill asked himself, and his mind reached back to his boyhood in the small village of Friendship, Maine. Even then he had been fascinated by mechanical things, figuring out how they worked and trying to fix them when they didn't. It was that love of tinkering that had later inspired him to become a pilot.

Bill remembered how he would often stop by on his way home from school to visit his father at the small factory he owned. One day his father had been very upset.

"I have a large order to get out, but three of my best men keep showing up late for work. It's throwing me behind."

"Are they sick?" Bill had asked.

"No, son, they're late because the bicycles they ride to work are broken. No one around here knows how to repair them."

"I could do it, Dad!" Bill said excitedly. "I know I could fix them! All I need are the right tools and a place to work here at the factory."

And that's how Bill got started working with machines. Every day after school and on most Saturdays and holidays he could be found in his shop straightening bent wheels, repairing broken chains, adjusting handlebars and brakes, and patching flat tires. He loved the work and was even able to save some money.

But Bill's real love was airplanes. This was during the early days of aviation when airplanes were little more than flying machines patched together out of cloth, a few sticks of wood, and metal wire. For power they used gasoline engines. With help from his younger brother Sterling, Bill started adapting marine engines (the engines used on boats) to make them work for airplanes.

One of Bill's greatest pleasures was going out to the local airfield to watch the airplanes he'd worked on fly through the air.

"I'd give anything to fly an airplane," he told Sterling one day. "Imagine what it must be like to see the world as birds do, free to go anywhere you want."

"Then why not take some flying lessons?" his brother said. "You're young and healthy. There's nothing stopping you!"

Bill agreed and soon found an instructor who taught him how to operate the rudder and the flaps, how to take off and land, how to bank and climb without stalling, and how to read the compass and altimeter. It wasn't long before he was a certified pilot. He then built his own airplane and started delivering the mail and giving people rides. As his skill increased, he began barnstorming around the countryside, showing off marvelous stunts like barrel rolls, lazy-eights, and loop-the-loops. He even flew upside down, and once, just for the thrill of it, he flew his airplane under the Brooklyn Bridge!

In time Sterling, too, became a pilot. The two brothers did a little barnstorming together and became friends with Charles Lindbergh, the first pilot in history to fly all the way across the Atlantic Ocean to Europe.

Then tragedy struck. Sterling was out flying when his engine suddenly quit, and he had to make a crash landing. He was killed. Bill and his young wife Edna were heartbroken. They were just starting a family, and the accident frightened her badly.

"Bill, I know you love flying, but it's just too risky," she told him. "You need to think about your family and how awful we'd feel if something happened to you."

He didn't want to hear what Edna had to say, but he knew she was right. So he quit flying and took a job as the captain of a lobster boat. It was hard, cold work and the hours were long, but it helped him keep his mind off his brother's death.

His love of flying never left him, though. From the deck of his boat he'd often watch an airplane shooting through the sky high above him. With a painful longing he'd remember the rush of the wind, the throb of the engine, and the feel of the control stick in his hand. He would see in his mind's eye the beauty of the distant horizon against the dark blue of the ocean. Some nights he would even dream about flying.

Finally an opportunity came his way that he felt he couldn't turn down. But he wanted Edna to approve the plan before he said yes, so he sat her down to talk it over.

"Dear," he began, "I know this flying business really scares you. I'll not deny it has its dangers. But it's what I enjoy doing more than anything else in the world." He waited a moment and then continued. "Glenn Curtiss came by to see me today. He offered me a job managing the flight service he's setting up here in Maine over in Rockland."

"Who's Glenn Curtiss?" she asked.

"Only the best airplane designer and builder in the United States, maybe the world. He'll supply the service with two of his latest airplanes. It's a wonderful opportunity!"

Edna was silent for a moment and then asked the one question he dreaded most to answer. "Will you have to fly, Bill?"

"Yes, Edna, that's part of the job. I'd be flying supplies, mail, and medicines a couple of times a week to some of the remote little communities along Penobscot Bay and up and down the coast. I'd be their link to the outside world. So you see, it's important work."

Edna thought long and hard before responding. Her emotions pulled her in different directions, but at last she said, "Well, I guess if you truly love someone, you should support him in whatever he needs to do. Just promise me you'll be careful, Bill. You have a son now who needs a father."

In his new job Bill flew an airplane (called a float plane) that didn't have any wheels. Instead, she was fitted out with two large pontoons, or floats, that enabled her to take off and land in the water. He hired a capable assistant, a man named Jack Dodge, and it wasn't long before the business was up and running and the two men were providing a much needed service to the citizens of Maine.

One December morning in 1929, a week before Christmas, Bill was loading his airplane with the day's deliveries when Jack showed up to lend him a hand. The waters of the bay were calm, but wintry clouds filled the sky. Jack was concerned.

"You know, Captain, I've been watching the windsock, and the wind has shifted around since last night. It's now coming in from the south, and that could mean a big storm is on the way."

Bill half suspected the same thing as he turned to look toward the distant ocean.

"It might be best to wait awhile and see what develops," Jack cautioned.

"But people are waiting for these deliveries. It'll be Christmas soon and they'll be wanting their cards and presents. If I hurry and don't stop for lunch, I'm pretty sure I can make it out to the tip of the bay and up along the coast and back before the storm hits. Pass me those last mail sacks."

Fifteen minutes later Bill was on his way. He flew along the edge of the bay until he reached the coast, where he turned east. Landing and taking off a number of times, he made his deliveries. But the winter storm was moving much faster than he'd expected. It caught up with him as he skirted the coast flying south, and now he was plowing through the heaviest snow he'd ever known. Violent gusts of wind threatened to tear the canvas right off his wings. It felt as if an angry giant had grabbed hold of his airplane and was trying to shake her to pieces. Bill was scared. He leaned in closer to the windshield, straining his eyes to see through the storm.

"I mustn't give up!" he said fiercely to himself. "I'll bring her down and see if I can get in under the worst of this. Maybe then I can figure out where I am."

He pushed the control stick forward to nose the airplane downward through the storm. She resisted for a moment, gave a shudder, and then started to lose altitude.

"Nice and easy now," Bill spoke to the airplane as if trying to calm a skittish horse. He felt the stick shake under his gloved hand as the powerful crosscurrents of wind buffeted the float plane. Lower and lower he descended, but still Bill could see nothing but white all around him. His greatest fear was that he might fly into the side of a mountain.

Then just below him he suddenly saw the angry whitecaps of enormous waves running with the storm. A shock of fear passed through him. He jerked back on the stick while pushing the throttle all the way forward. The airplane roared and lurched back up into the sky. Bill's heart was beating furiously, and his hand on the stick was trembling. It had been a very close call and he knew it.

"Well, old gal," he gasped," at least we found out one thing — we're over water, not land." Talking to the airplane somehow helped him steady his nerves and not feel so all alone. He looked at the fuel gauge again. The needle continued to drop, and with a sickening feeling he realized his fuel was almost gone. He thought again of his wife and son. How he wished he could hug them both and tell them how much

he loved them!

Then something caught his eye through the blinding snow. It was a flash of light. He turned his airplane toward it and then saw it again. It was a lighthouse! Bill's heart filled with hope.

A number of lighthouses stood along the coast to warn ships at sea that they were approaching land. Bill knew that each lighthouse had its own special way of flashing its light to let ships know exactly where they were. By counting the seconds between flashes, he realized that he was seeing the Dice Head Lighthouse near the head of Penobscot Bay. He reasoned that he could find his way home by following the lighthouses that were located along the edge of the bay.

Turning as he came over the Dice Head Lighthouse, Bill flew through the storm until he spotted the light from the Fort Point Lighthouse. From there he continued flying south to the Grindle Point Lighthouse and then on to the lighthouses at Curtis Island and Indian Island. All the time he was looking anxiously at the falling needle of his fuel gauge.

Finally off to his left in the distance he spied the Owl's Head Lighthouse and before him the Rockland Breakwater Lighthouse at the mouth of Rockland Harbor. He was home! Just as he touched down on the water, his engine sputtered and quit. He'd run completely out of fuel.

"Well, old girl," Bill heaved a huge sigh of relief as the airplane rocked quietly on the water, "you got us back, safe and sound."

Through the blowing snow he could see Jack bringing up the tractor to pull the airplane out of the water — and a welcome sight he was!

The storm blew itself out during the night, and the next morning at breakfast Bill told his wife and son Billy about his harrowing experience.

"Without the lighthouses to guide me I would surely have been lost," he said. "You know, I've been thinking about those poor lighthouse keepers and their families. They must lead awfully lonely lives, stuck way out there by themselves with no neighbors, no stores, and no schools for the young ones to go to. Christmas might be a bit dreary for them, I would think."

"Well, they certainly have *my* gratitude," said Edna. "And think about all the sailors who rely on them. If the lighthouse keepers didn't keep the lights fueled, the wicks trimmed, and the lenses cleaned year in and year out, there'd be many a ship going down and many a sailor with her."

An expression of determination suddenly came over Bill's features. "I've just had an idea — a capital idea!"

"What is it, Dad?"

"Let's play Santa Claus for those families — bring them a little Christmas cheer." He stood up and threw his napkin on the table.

"Come on, you two! Grab your coats, we're going to town!"

The snow-covered roads made it slow going in the truck, but at last they made it. They went directly to the general store.

"Morning, George, and Merry Christmas!" Bill greeted the store owner with a broad smile.

"And Merry Christmas to you folks," replied George pleasantly. "What brings you to town?"

"We need to do some last minute holiday shopping," said Edna.

"I should be able to help with that. What kinds of gifts are you looking for?"

"Let's start with some books," Bill said and he scanned the tall shelves behind the counter. "Good books for a family to enjoy together. And cans of coffee, tea, and cocoa. Yes, and some playing cards too."

Edna jumped in. "We'll need some sewing notions: packets of needles, an assortment of buttons, and spools of colored thread."

"And don't forget toys — yo-yos and jacks and crayons and coloring books." Billy was sure he knew best what the children would want.

"And some hard candy, George — half a bushel if you've got it," put in Bill.

The look on George's face registered such speechless bewilderment at the size and variety of the order that all three Wincapaws burst out laughing.

"We haven't gone crazy," Bill assured him. "It's for the lighthouse keepers and their families. They saved my life in last night's storm, and we mean to repay them with a little Christmas surprise!"

Bill also bought several bales of marsh hay and seven heavy burlap sacks.

Back at home the Wincapaws divided the gifts equally and placed them into the seven sacks. They tied a thick layer of marsh hay around each sack, making it into a tight bundle. The hay would act as padding and help the bundles to float should they somehow fall in the water.

Christmas day dawned clear and bright. The sky was blue and cloudless, a perfect day for flying. With

the help of Edna, Billy, and Jack, Bill loaded the big burlap bundles into the float plane.

"Billy, I'll need you to go along with me to act as bombardier. Do you think you can manage it?"

"I sure can!" Billy looked uncertainly at his mother. "Is it all right for me to go, Mom?"

Edna nodded and Billy climbed excitedly into the airplane.

With a roar and a puff of bluish-black smoke the airplane's engine came to life. Edna had to grab her hat to keep it from blowing off in the wind from the propeller. Wheeling around in the water, Bill pointed the airplane down the harbor and took off into the morning sun.

"Are we going to land at each lighthouse?" Billy yelled over the noise of the engine.

"That would take too long, son. No, we'll drop the bundles from the air next to each lighthouse."

"But how will the lighthouse keepers know to look for them?"

"We'll fly low and buzz them first to get their attention."

It wasn't long before they approached the Owl's Head Lighthouse. Bill banked the airplane so she swung low around the tall structure. On the second pass they could see the lighthouse keeper and his wife come outside and look up at them, shielding their eyes from the sun with their hands.

"They see us now," said Bill. "Open the window, son, and push out a bundle when I tell you to." Billy had never done anything so exciting before in his life. He held a sack stuffed with presents half out the window as his father came down low. He could see the waves washing up against the rocks below them.

"Now!" his father shouted as he pulled back on the control stick to regain altitude. Billy pushed the bundle free and watched it land next to the lighthouse.

"Good job, son," said Bill with satisfaction. "Let's get on to the next lighthouse."

"Whatever you say, Santa!" Billy was grinning from ear to ear.

That day Captain Wincapaw and his son delivered seven Christmas bundles to seven very surprised and grateful lighthouse families. A couple of days later thank you letters from the lighthouse keepers began appearing in the local newspapers. The letters spoke of how lonely life at a lighthouse could be and how much the unexpected presents had meant to those who received them.

Bill and his family were so happy they decided to continue with what they'd started. The next year they delivered more presents to the lighthouses. In fact, delivering the presents soon became a Christmas tradition, and each year more and more lighthouses were added to the list.

And some funny things happened too.

One time a strong gust of wind caught a bundle as it was dropped from the airplane and carried it straight through the skylight of a lighthouse kitchen. It landed on the table, and the mother said calmly, "Well, I guess we can celebrate our Christmas now."

Over time people started calling Captain Wincapaw the "Flying Santa." Companies began donating some of the presents and the fuel for his airplane. And when Billy turned sixteen, he became one of the youngest licensed pilots in the state and made some of the Christmas flights on his own.

And there have been other Flying Santas over the years. Edward Rowe Snow was a high school teacher, historian, and writer of sea stories. After flying a couple of times with the Wincapaws, he offered to take over. For over four decades he chartered airplanes with professional pilots and delivered the Christmas presents to the lighthouses with his wife Anna Myrle and daughter Dolly. He would even include copies of his own books in the gift bundles.

Today the tradition of the Flying Santa lives on. Although many of the lighthouses are now automated, volunteers who call themselves "The Friends of Flying Santa" continue to deliver Christmas presents by helicopter to the children of Coast Guard families at thirty-five stations in six states.

Bill Wincapaw did many exciting things during his lifetime as a pilot. But the one that meant the most to him and to many, many others was being the first Flying Santa.